KT-237-928

This Book Belongs to

....

I celebrated World Book Day 2015
with this brilliant gift from my
local bookseller and Templar Publishing.

A Pirate's Guide to LANDLUBBING

JONNY DUDDLE

templar

A TEMPLAR BOOK

First published in the UK in 2015 by Templar Publishing,
an imprint of The Templar Company Limited,
Deepdene Lodge, Deepdene Avenue, Dorking, Surrey, RH5 4AT, UK
www.templarco.co.uk

First edition

MIX
Paper from
responsible sources
FSC® C003532
FSC
www.fsc.org

ISBN 978-1-78370-181-0

Designed by Hannah Mee
Edited by Katie Haworth

Printed in the UK

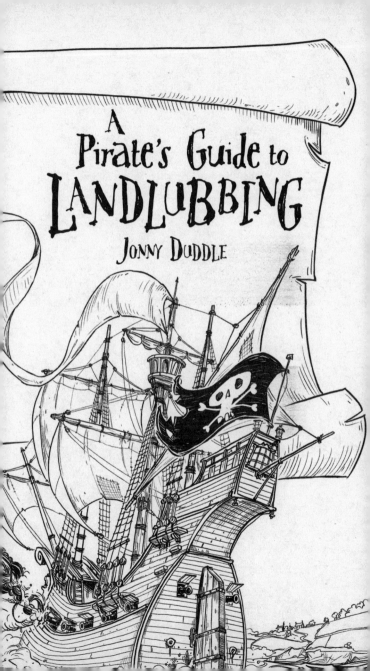

A Pirate's Guide to LANDLUBBING

JONNY DUDDLE

Ahoy, ye scurvy seadogs!

I ain't much of a lubber, but this year I visited the seaside town of Dull-on-Sea with my folks, the Jolley-Rogers.

Now y'might wonder why a family of cutlass-waving pirates would holiday without the waves beneath their feet, but my dad was fixin' our ship and we was marooned for a while, with nowt but lubbers for company. I ain't sayin' I'm an expert, but I made some friends and we did a bit of explorin' and in the end I was sad to leave.

So this is my guide to landlubbing, for any who fancy an excursion ashore.

Ahoy and Avast!
Jim Lad

Contents

1: A History of Dull-on-Sea
(Stuff What I Learned at School)

2: Steppin' Ashore

3: Gettin' Around on Dry Ground

4: Stuff to See

5: How to Tell a Lubber
from a Pirate

6: Parley Like a Lubber!

7: Lubber Etiquette with Nugget

8: Grul and Grog

9: Rest Ye Weary Bones
(Places to Stay)

10: Keepin' on the Right Side of the Law

The Sea Calls...

1.

A History of Dull-on-Sea

(Stuff What I Learned at School)

The first settlers arrived in the Stone Age. They used bits of flint and pebbles off the beach to make pointy things for killing bears and deer.

They caught fish too, and liked paddling, sunbathing and hanging out in caves. After a thousand years or so of chipping stones, one bright spark found some copper in the ground and, with a bit of clever smelting, he made everyone bronze tips for their spears. These were even better for killing bears and deer.

Bronze made excellent arrow tips too, so even bunny rabbits weren't safe.

A few years later, their weapons were also good for repelling Romans and the local tribe earned a fearsome reputation. By now, they'd built houses and liked to grow vegetables, farm livestock and go fishing in little boats. They enjoyed a good bonfire and worshipped lots of different gods.

So, for many years, the local folk were an exciting, independent bunch and very fond of parties, dressing up and sacrifices.

But in AD 894, their fun was ended by the ferocious Viking, Dulrick the Dull. Dulrick banned parties, silly costumes and dancing, and decreed that everyone should eat healthy food, drink warm milk and go to bed early.

He ate all the sheep brains, washed down with milk, and named the town 'Dull-on-Sea'.

Many long, tedious years later, Dulrick returned to Vikingland because he missed fjords, his mum and watching icicles grow.

Most of his crew remained in Dull-on-Sea because they couldn't face the long journey back, and the prospect of Dulrick's endless games of 'I spy' with nothing to see but the ocean and the odd puffin.

They promised Dulrick that they would maintain the Viking laws and that they wouldn't let anyone go to bed too late. But no sooner had Dulrick disappeared over the horizon, than the Vikings married local girls, who loved to party.

Before long, Dull-on-Sea was renowned for all-night shindigs, mead drinking and moonlit swims.

This attracted a motley bunch of villains and rogues and for a few centuries Dull-on-Sea was a devilish place. In the eighteenth century the town became a hive of piracy and smuggling. No ship was safe if it passed within view of Dull-on-Sea, especially if it was laden with a precious cargo.

Guns and gold and fine French brandy were brought ashore beyond the reach and taxes of King George's navy.

The king was a bit miffed about all this, so he sent his finest officer, Admiral George Fellowes, to sort out the town for good.

Once again, the fun abruptly stopped.

In the harbour, Royal Navy frigates replaced pirate ships, and Admiral Fellowes cleaned up the streets of Dull-on-Sea.

As the Victorian age dawned, a train line was built and city folk flocked to the guesthouses and safe sands, where they sunbathed (fully clothed), strolled up and down the new pier and sipped tea in the promenade cafes, whilst munching on scones and clotted cream.

Admiral George Fellowes put the 'dull' back in Dull-on-Sea, and it has changed little since.

But don't let that put ye scurvy dogs off. Even a pirate can enjoy a scone or two.

2.
STEPPIN' ASHORE

On the approach to Dull-on-Sea, ye'll be noticin' the lighthouse. Ye might be transfixed by the sparkly light, but best avoid it because it's a warnin' of some perilous rocks that'd shipwreck ye good and proper!

So, steer yer ship a bit to the left and ye can moor in the harbour.

Try not to squash any fishing boats – that'd just make the fishermen grumpy and ye'd be chased back to sea before ye'd furled yer mainsail!

On the harbourside ye'll be spyin' a few inns. Best be avoidin' these if ye want yer trip ashore to be a success. I ain't met a pirate yet, who don't get a bit rowdy after tippin' some grog down their gullet.

To get yer bearings, ye can grab a map from the Tourist Information hut on the promenade and explore Dull-on-Sea's streets and alleyways to yer heart's content.

Grog! Grub! Shanties!

3.
GETTIN' AROUND ON DRY GROUND

Once ashore, a ship's no good to ye, and ye'll be looking for some other way to get around.

Perhaps the easiest way to explore Dull-on-Sea is on foot (or a wooden leg if ye've been unlucky). But, if yer peg leg is weary, ye could try a bicycle.

Bicycles are a cursed lubber contraption with two wheels. They take a bit of balancin', which can be tricky if ye've just set ashore and are wobblin' with land-sickness...

Ye could try a bike with stabilisers, but these tend to be on the small side so ye'll be needin' something bigger. Ye can go with the latest high-tech bicycle, with a kerzwillion gears and bouncing back end, but if ye'd be wantin' a better view, then ye might have more luck with a penny farthing, available to hire on the Victorian pier.

A word of warning, once ye've started pedalling, ye'll need to keep going or ye'll be keeling over and ye may be needin' a new wooden leg or two.

Other options available
include scooters, skateboards and
roller-skates, but I've yet to meet a
pirate who has the balancin' ability
for those blighters.

For those who have a driving
licence, like this...

DRIVING LICENCE ASHORE

1. SILVER
2. LONG JOHN
3. 23.05.1883
4A. 24.03.2018   4B. ROAD SAFETY
AUTHORITY

5. B123456
7. LONG JOHN SILVER
8. THE HISPANIOLA

P1 RAT

not this...

This letter of marque hereby
certifies that

Long John Silver

Has licence to raid, plunder
and pillage. Avast!

...ye could hire yer'self a moped.

Mopeds take no effort from yer legs and tootle along with only petrol to keep 'em goin'. Ye'll need to wear a helmet, so if ye have a spectacular head of hair, with beads and wotnot, don't forget a bobble or two to tie it out of the way. And ye'll need a box on the back for yer pirate hat and feathers.

There are cars to hire too. Ye can fit more pirates in a car than ye can on a moped, but don't stuff too many in, or ye'll be attracting the interest of the Law who'll want to know if yer seatbelts are all plugged in.

If driving yer'self seems too dangerous, then ye'd be better on the bus. There are single-storey buses with roofs, which are nice enough, but even better are the great tall ones with an upstairs where ye can see the sky. Take yer strongest umbrella though, for the weather of Dull-on-Sea ain't so kind.

4.
STUFF TO SEE

Dull-on-Sea is full of landlubber houses. Believe it or not, land-lovin' folk actually live in these. They don't have to tie themselves to the mast if it's blowin' a gale, they don't worry about seasickness and they don't poop out of their windows.

Which might be soundin' good after a long voyage with a heavin' tummy and a cold posterior, but they're stuck in one place all the time, even when it's rainin', and where's the fun in that?

Tucked amongst the houses, there's plenty for a pirate to see!

Dull-on-Sea Museum

Right by the harbour is Dull-on-Sea Museum. It's full of precious things that ye ain't allowed to touch, although a lot of it looks like rotten old flotsam and jetsam to me.

The cannons don't look like they've fired in hundreds of years and the bits of the ship they've got have been half-eaten by the scurvy sea!

Don't be takin' nothin' shiny from the museum or ye'll be answerin' to the Law!

THE LIBRARY

Dull-on-Sea Library is brimful of books, it's a treasure trove of words!

Now, the problem with words is that not many of ye seafarers can read that well, so best visit the children's section. Children's books have less words and plenty of pictures, and there are a lot more stories about pirates and runnin' folk through.

Grown ups do like to read books about grisly murders, but there's rarely a cutlass involved and they're always about love and kissin' and stuff.

Bleurgh...

If yer very lucky, ye may arrive at storytime, when one of the librarians reads a book out loud. Maybe take a seat behind the children, so the nippers can see the book all right.

And be on yer best behaviour. Librarians are a fearsome bunch and don't take kindly to rambunctious behaviour, flintlock firing or sea shanties.

At least not when they're at work...

THE PARK

If ye'd like to clear the brine from yer nostrils and ye have a fondness for ducks, I'd recommend the park.

There's a playground, a bandstand and lots of flowers. Dad likes to drive our amphibious jeep in the boating lake, but the park warden gets all uppity. So now we just visit in the middle of the night, when we go to bury treasure on the bowling green.

A word of warnin' if ye like to walk around barefoot, ye might want to watch out for dog poo...

SHOPPIN'!

Being on dry land is the perfect opportunity for stockin' up on provisions and buyin' some new clothes to replace yer scurvy rags.

There be hat shops too, but they don't stock much of a pirate-y nature.

I still ain't found the gunpowder shop.

School

Ye can't come visitin' my school
unless yer under ten years old.
And if ye *are* under ten, ye need to
be able to sit all quiet and listen to
stuff. I find it pretty tricky, and I'm
always being told that I should wear
shoes and that my uniform is wrong.

All the kids dress the same and
sit in rows learnin' stuff all day. But
I have to leave my cutlass at home,
because sword fightin' ain't in the
curriculum.

They don't even teach knots, rope climbin' or how to load a cannon. I doubt any of the teachers have spent even a day on the rollin' ocean.

They don't seem to teach much that's useful to pirates, although I do like history and art's my favourite, because I get to draw maps and sea monsters on big bits of paper.

5.
How to Tell a Lubber from a Pirate

It's not too hard to spot a pirate in a town of lubbers.

Lubbers tend to have lots of teeth, neatly combed hair and clothes that don't smell too bad. Those that don hats wear small ones with a distinct lack of gold, feathers or skulls.

Most lubbers are modest with their

jewellery and don't fill their belts with cutlasses and flintlocks.

Dull-on-Sea Police don't take kindly to weapons, so remember to leave them on yer ship! Leavin' their weapons at home is probably why lubbers ain't covered in scars and most of 'em appear to have all their limbs attached.

I ain't noticed one yet with a hook for a hand or a wooden leg. The only eyepatch I've seen was a kid with glasses, who assured me she had an eye underneath it and the patch was goin' to make it work better.

Landlubbers like to keep their fingernails clean and brush their teeth twice a day, with gunk called toothpaste. It makes their teeth gleam, and it keeps their breath from smelling like rat-infested bilges. They have different pets too. None of my lubber friends have monkeys or parrots. They spend half their time walkin' dogs, which come in all shapes and sizes, and pickin' up poo in little plastic bags.

LUBBER

They also like tickling cats until the cats get all grumpy and claw 'em like their hand is a ship's rat.

Can ye spot the differences...?

PIRATE

6.
PARLEY LIKE A LUBBER!

Yer goin' to struggle to talk to lubbers if ye can't speak their language, and they don't half talk funny...

Ye'll be wantin' to learn some lubber phrases, like those on the followin' pages.

Or get yer'self a clever parrot that can do the talkin' for ye.

Pieces of Eight!

I'm rather peckish.
I do believe it's lunchtime.
Could you pour me a pineapple and soda water, please barman?
A single to Dull-on-Sea Museum, please Mr Bus Conductor!

7.

LUBBER ETIQUETTE WITH NUGGET

I'm Jim Lad's little sister, Nugget, and since I've been livin' in Dull-on-Sea, I've been mostly learnin' my good manners. This is the important stuff:

No firing cannons on a Sunday mornin'! Lubbers like peace and quiet, long lie-ins and readin' the paper.

No tying up the postman. Or makin' him walk the plank.

No choppin' heads off gnomes.

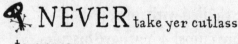 Don't bury yer dad's car keys,
unless yer really good at drawin' maps.

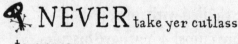 Don't bury yer neighbour's car,
unless you can dig real quick.

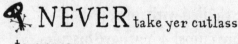 NEVER take yer cutlass
to nursery.

8.
GRUB AND GROG

Ye may be used to hard tack on yer long sails, but lubber biscuits are more appealin' than yer hard, stale, maggot-riddled ship's biscuit. If they're riddled with 'owt, it'll be chocolate chips! They have biscuits with jam in the middle! Biscuits filled with custard! Pink biscuits!

And ye can't beat a biscuit dunked in tea. Lubbers love tea. If they ain't stuffin' their faces with scones or cake, they'll be dunkin' biscuits.

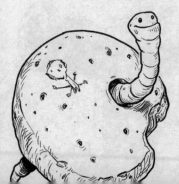

But biscuits ain't a proper meal to fill yer tummy. There are lots of cafes and restaurants in the streets of Dull-on-Sea, but it's probably best ye stick to takeaways because no doubt yer table manners ain't so good. I'd recommend the fish and chips.

And don't forget to order some mushy peas on the side. They're a bit like the hot snot that dribbles from yer nostrils on a cold winter's day, but they taste even better.

Since I been landlubbing, I've developed a liking for '99' cornets, with a big stick of flaky chocolate pokin' out the top and blood-red sauce dribbled all over.

If yer a pirate with a dairy intolerance, and yer crew are enjoying ice creams, there's always a good selection of ice lollies to choose from.

Pirates with teeth should try some Dull-on-Sea rock. Not so easy to eat if yer a bit gummy, but ye could just suck on a stick for a few hours. Or ye may find candyfloss yer best bet, although it's hard to look menacing with a fluffy pink ball in one hand.

For health-conscious pirates, who ain't particular to sweets, ye could eat a bit of fruit and get that scurvy sorted.

9.
REST YE
WEARY BONES
(Places to Stay)

Durin' yer stay in Dull-on-Sea, ye
could sleep aboard yer ship if she's
moored in the harbour. But if ye'd like
the full landlubbing experience, then
try sleepin' on dry land.

Dull-on-Sea is full of hotels and
guesthouses. Hotels have lots
of rooms. If ye ain't good
at rememberin' numbers,
ye should probably draw
a map before ye go out
so ye can find yer room
when ye come back.

Or ye could tie a piece of string to yer door-handle and the other end to yer wooden leg, which should make it easy to find yer way back. It's very easy to upset other guests. Seaside hotels are normally full of old folk hopin' for a quiet weekend, who might be disgruntled by a noisy pirate crew, hollerin' and singin' and drinkin' grog.

Guesthouses are lubber houses that let ye rent a room for the night. There'll be less rooms than in a hotel, so there'll be less folk to upset!

OOO-ARR!

MISTY VIEW
GUESTHOUSE
VACANCIES

No PIRA

Caravans are popular at the seaside, and they're a bit like rectangular ships with nice cushions. They don't float though, so don't try launchin' yer caravan in the sea if ye decide ye like it.

Caravans are often quite close together and they all look the same, so maybe try the string trick, or paint a big skull-and-crossbones on the side to find it easily after a day out.

If yer short of gold, or like the sound of flappin' canvas, ye can stay in a tent.

But don't sing yer shanties too loud at bedtime, or the whole campsite will hear.

The same goes for snoring.

And trumping.

10.
Keepin' on the Right Side of the Law

The Dull-on-Sea Police would like to say a few things:

Good day, Pirates! Here at Dull-on-Sea Police we keep a tight ship. We have rules. We know that pirates struggle sometimes with sticking to rules, but we'd like you to have a nice vacation in Dull-on-Sea without seeing the inside of a prison cell.

NO CUTLASSES, especially not at nursery.

NO CANNON FIRING, especially not on a Sunday morning.

NO SHANTIES after 11.00 pm. We like to go to bed early in Dull-on-Sea and get upset when we hear other people having fun.

Please leave the gold in the museum. **IT'S NOT YOURS.**

NO SWORD FIGHTING please, even if the other gentleman insulted your monkey friend.

NO MERMAIDS in the swimming pool.

NO POOPING out of windows.

THE SEA CALLS...

A pirate soon misses the gentle bob of the sea, and ye can't be landlubbing forever.

As I like to say:

Pirates need adventure,
to see lands across the ocean!
We need cutlasses and treasure
maps and lots of suntan lotion!

But if ye've had a grand time, please tell yer pirate friends about Dull-on-Sea! The more lubbers meet us pirate-types, the more they'll realise we're a bit like them, just with cutlasses, cannons and a murderous glint in our eyes.

FAIR VOYAGE, ME HEARTY!

Chapter one

For the fourth morning in a row, when Bob, the Man on the Moon, woke up, he wasn't tucked up in the cosy bed where he'd fallen asleep. Instead, he found himself curled tightly in a ball in what seemed like some kind of tiny house. Gingerly, he wriggled out through its small door and quickly realised that the tiny house was actually his dog Barry's kennel. He would have been surprised had he not woken on the three previous mornings in the bath, the airing cupboard and the potting shed. The unusual was becoming quite usual.

Barry himself wasn't anywhere to be seen. In fact, Bob's best-ever friend had been missing for three days. He had disappeared, without warning, around the time Bob's sleepwalking had begun. Bob was convinced that there was a link between the two. However, he wasn't sure whether the sleepwalking had somehow scared Barry away, or whether the sleepwalking had actually been caused by the worry of Barry's disappearance. Either way, Bob was upset. Why would Barry leave him?

Bob missed his best-ever friend so much. All around the house there were reminders of him – his rubber bone, his basket, his ball, his bobble balaclava. And curiously too, the smell of dog was becoming stronger, not weaker. Even Bob's pyjamas seemed to stink of pooch. Stranger still, considering Bob had completely lost his appetite, they were also caked in gravy stains, barbecue sauce and meaty grease. The kitchen too was littered with the bony remains of chicken drumsticks, spare ribs, T-bone steaks and lamb

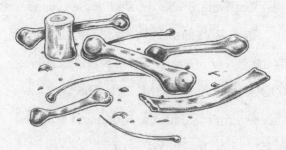

chops. It was a mystery indeed.

Just looking at the mess made Bob feel itchy and no amount of scratching could soothe him. In truth though, it was probably the pesky space dust that was irritating him. Ever since the big scary, hairy asteroid had collided with the Moon, he hadn't been able to scrub it off, not even with his Spacedust Superloofah.

Bob had noticed the asteroid whilst vacuuming the lunar landscape four days earlier. He'd watched, open-mouthed, as it zoomed in from deep space at a blistering pace, its long, red mane trailing elegantly behind it. But there had been nothing elegant about what happened next. Realising it was on a collision course with the Moon, Bob and Barry had leapt, headlong, for the safety of crater 1973. Seconds later… BOOOOOOOOOMMM!!!!!!! The big, scary, hairy asteroid had hit the Moon and bounced back out into the darkness of space. For more than an hour, the universe had shook.

When Bob and Barry had finally re-emerged it was onto a lunar surface shrouded in a pea-souper fog of space-dust, the like of which Bob had never seen before. Worse, until the lunar mist cleared, he would have no idea how much damage had been done to his beloved Moon. For hours the dust had swirled and whirled and crept into any nook and cranny it could find. Even Bob's Moon suit, boots and helmet were no protection. He'd begun to itch immediately and hadn't stopped since.

Bob had been back home for days now, and he was becoming convinced that somehow the asteroid was to blame for triggering the mysterious events – the sleepwalking, the messy house, Barry's disappearance – not to mention the constant itching and scratching.

SPONSORED BY

WORLD BOOK DAY
5 MARCH 2015

WORLD BOOK DAY *fest*

A BIG, HAPPY, BOOKY CELEBRATION OF READING

》 Want to READ more? 《

VISIT your local bookshop

- Get some great recommendations for what to read next
- Meet your favourite authors & illustrators at brilliant events
- Discover books you never even knew existed!

FIND YOUR LOCAL BOOKSHOP www.booksellers.org.uk/bookshopsearch

JOIN your local library

You can browse and borrow from a HUGE selection of books and get recommendations of what to read next from expert librarians—all for **FREE**! You can also discover libraries' wonderful children's and family reading activities.

FIND YOUR LOCAL LIBRARY www.findalibrary.co.uk

Get ONLINE!

Visit WORLDBOOKDAY.COM to discover a whole new world of books!

- Downloads and activities for **FAB** books and authors
- Cool games, trailers and videos
- Author events in your area
- News, competitions and new books —all in a **FREE** monthly email

and MORE!